BRITISH PLANT LIFE

MOSSES AND LIVERWORTS OF WOODLAND

A Guide to Some of the Commonest Species

A. Roy Perry

AMGUEDDFA GENEDLAETHOL CYMRU
NATIONAL MUSEUM OF WALES

Cardiff 1992

First published March, 1992
© National Museum of Wales
Cathays Park
Cardiff CF1 3NP

Copyright of the colour
photographs remains with
the photographers

ISBN 0 7200 0362 8

Production: Hywel G. Rees
Artwork: Pica, Cardiff
Typesetting: Afal, Cardiff
Type: Baskerville 9/10pt
Printing: McLays, Cardiff

This series of books on British plants produced by the Department of Botany of
the National Museum of Wales is an introduction to the extremely diverse plant
life to be found in the British Isles. It is the hope of the authors that through
its pages the reader will be left with a greater appreciation of the subject and
beauty of the natural world and be stimulated to explore further the realms of
British plants perhaps as yet unknown to him.

Cover photograph: Wistman's Wood, Devon (*M.C.F. Proctor*)

Introduction

The primary aim of this small book is to provide a simple, photographic guide to some of the more common mosses and liverworts to be found in woodlands in the British Isles. Encouragement for this project has been provided by many naturalists and beginners who have for some time asked about the availability of such a guide to help them get to know some of the species that they encounter during the course of their rambles in the countryside. Any other habitat beside woodland might have been chosen for this introduction; but woodland is a friendly habitat in which the mosses and liverworts encountered, especially in the wetter western parts of these islands, are conspicuous and well-grown, and many of them are not difficult to identify when a little familiarity has been acquired. In addition, mosses and liverworts, unlike most flowering plants, lend themselves to investigation all the year round; indeed they are sometimes more easily detected, especially on the woodland floor, when the herbaceous vegetation has died down in winter. So they are a convenient group to study.

A serious limitation of such a guide as this is that not every species that one is likely to come across can be included and inevitably those people using it will soon discover a moss or liverwort that fails to match up with any included here. But when this happens it should be seen as progress! It should be pointed out that species common on limestone boulders in calcareous habitats but uncommon to rare elsewhere, are not included; perhaps these may be the subject of a future booklet in this series. Instead, prominence has been given to species common in acidic woodlands.

The book contains black and white photographs of 21 species of mosses and of 8 species of liverworts. These 29 species are amongst the most widespread and abundant bryophytes - especially in woodland habitats - in the British Isles. For each species a description of the main features of the plant are given by which it may be identified in the field, in addition to notes on its abundance and habitat. Emphasis is on identification in the field: microscopic characters have not been included and, if required, should be sought in more advanced texts (see Further Reading, rear cover). However, aspiring field bryologists should arm themselves with a pocket lens of x10 magnification and be prepared to use it, as some species, though easily recognized, are very small. Some people manage with a x8 lens, but they see less! Others use x20 but beginners may find the use of such a lens difficult, at least in the early stages.

Each species description is accompanied by a map showing the distribution of the plant in the British Isles. In the maps the solid black patches represent widespread and common occurrence, the grey patches frequent occurrence, the unshaded patches absence. Several line drawings are supplied to aid recognition and interpretation of the photographs and descriptions. Each unit of the scale bars represents 1 mm. A supplement to the main text is colour photographs of ten other common species of mosses and liverworts.

The general life history of mosses and liverworts is the same. The leafy shoots give rise to male ($\male$) and to female ($\female$) sex organs, in some species on the same shoot (Fig. 1), in others on different shoots (Fig. 2). In simple terms the male organs produce sperm cells and the female organs produce egg cells. Sperms are released and, attracted by a chemical secretion, swim towards the female in the layer of moisture on the plant surface. Fertilization of an egg cell by a sperm takes place, and results in a zygote which develops and eventually grows into a capsule (the "fruit") which is normally borne on a longish stalk (called the seta) embedded in the leafy plant that gave rise to the original egg cell. The end-product of many cell-divisions within the capsule is numerous dust-like spores which when ripe are shed from the capsule and dispersed by air currents. Each spore on germination may give rise to a new colony of moss or liverwort.

The beginner will need to familiarize himself with the differences between the two classes of bryophytes. The following are some differences between mosses and liverworts that may be seen in the field.

1. If the bryophyte consists of a flattened shoot not differentiated into stem and leaves (a thallus) it is a liverwort, as all mosses have leaves (Fig. 3). However, it should be noted that most liverworts are leafy, too.

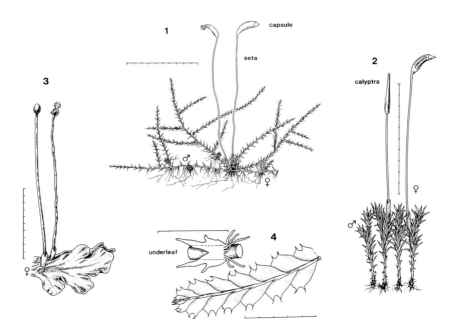

Fig. 1: The moss *Amblystegium serpens* showing male and female inflorescences produced on the same shoot. One of the capsules has shed its lid. In the other the lid remains. Fig. 2: The moss *Ceratodon purpureus* showing separate male and female plants. Of the two capsules the ripe one on the right still retains its lid and is furrowed; the other, less mature, has a calyptra. Fig. 3: *Pellia epiphylla*, a thallose liverwort, showing two capsules on long setae, one dehisced, the other ready for dehiscence. Fig. 4. The leafy liverwort *Lophocolea bidentata* showing bilobed lateral leaves on one stem and an underleaf on part of another.

2. If the leaves are divided into lobes or segments the plant is a liverwort (Fig. 4). However, although mosses do not have lobed or segmented leaves, there are many leafy liverworts with undivided leaves (see pp. 38 and 39).

3. Leafy liverworts have the leaves normally arranged in three rows on the stem, two of the rows being lateral and the third row (the underleaves), usually much smaller than the lateral leaves, on the underside of the stem (Fig. 4). The underleaves are sometimes rather too small to be seen without a microscope and in some species they are missing entirely. Most mosses have their leaves spirally arranged on the stem. However, a very few, for example *Fissidens* species (see p. 10), have a two-ranked leaf arrangement and thus look, superficially at least, like some leafy liverworts. *Fissidens* species are usually easily identified as mosses in the field by using a lens; then the clear presence of a thickened midrib (costa), a structure that no leafy liverworts possess, will be seen. There are many moss species without single midribs of this sort but their leaf arrangement, or some other character, can usually be used in deciding whether they are mosses or liverworts.

4. The fruiting structures of mosses and liverworts are quite different. That of a liverwort usually consists of a weak, transparent seta bearing a spherical or ovoid capsule on top (Fig. 3), the whole being produced from within a tubular perianth, a structure composed of modified leaves which serves to protect the female sex organs and the young developing capsule; when ripe the liverwort capsule opens not by a lid but by four splits, releases the spores over a short period, then shrivels and dies. In the majority of mosses, on the other hand, the fruit consists of a tough wiry seta, and an often cylindrical or pear-shaped capsule with a distinct apical lid (Figs. 1,2); there is no perianth; when the spores are ripe the lid is shed and the spores are discharged over a quite long period, the old fruit often remaining on the parent plant for many months, sometimes until the following year's crop of fruit is produced.

There are many exceptions to the foregoing which is a simplified account of the usual structures to be met with in the field in mosses and liverworts and the usual course of events during spore production and discharge. These will be discovered as the beginner gets more knowledgeable.

5. Many other differences between mosses and liverworts will be seen only by using a microscope. For a description of these the reader is referred to more specialized books.

In the British Isles there are around 700 different mosses and 300 different liverworts, so the 39 species included in this guide are but a small proportion of the total. However, it should be stated that many of the British species are very rare or local, occurring in only one or two localities or areas; so they are not likely to be seen by the beginner unless specially sought. A great number of other species, too, are confined to special habitats such as bogs and exposed alpine rocks and will not be found unless these habitats are explored.

In this guide mosses are dealt with first, then liverworts. To make it easier to place a moss those species with simple or little-branched stems which grow erect and are not intricately mixed with their neighbours are first described; these are followed by those species that have strongly branched stems often confusedly intermixed with each other and form wefts or mats. The liverworts start with a thallose species and end with leafy types whose leaf shape and arrangement on the stem are very important in identification.

Pogonatum aloides (x 1.5)

Capsules are frequently produced by this moss and it is then readily identified. They are borne on an upright red seta up to about 25 mm high and when young each is covered by a shaggy greenish-brown calyptra. The thick, opaque leaves are toothed at the margins. When barren the very short, usually unbranched stems, usually no more than 15 mm high (and often shorter), are very distinctive and resemble miniature aloe plants growing on bare clayey soil. It is a common species of woodland, especially in the west and north. Preferring acidic soils, it forms dark green open turfs on near-vertical clay banks and cuttings, as on ditch-sides, and newly disturbed soil (on which it is a pioneer) such as on upturned roots of fallen trees. It is also found at roadsides in moorland districts. Its leafy stems arise from a persistent alga-like protonema which covers the substrate and may usually be seen between the plants. A pioneer species it is rarely associated with other species of bryophytes.

Polytrichum formosum (x 1.3)

In woods, where it forms tall, loose, dark green tufts or turfs composed of stiff, erect stems up to about 100 mm tall (but frequently less), this is a common species. Its rigid, pointed leaves spread out from the stem and have toothed margins and its capsules, which are commonly produced and when ripe are 5-6 angled, are borne on setae up to 75 mm high. It grows typically on the ground in deciduous woodland and likes heavy acidic soils though it will tolerate nearly neutral conditions. *Polytrichum formosum* is less frequently found growing on heath and moorland, the usual habitat of a close relative, *P. commune*, with which it may then be confused. However, the sheathing leaf bases of *P. formosum* do not have the silvery sheen seen in *P. commune* and the capsules of the latter are only 4-angled.

Atrichum undulatum (x 1.2)

By its narrow tongue-shaped, wavy leaves up to 8 mm long and sharply toothed at the margin, this common moss is easy to recognize. Each stem is simple, upright and up to about 50 mm tall and often bears at its apex, on a red seta up to 40 mm tall, a conspicuous narrow strongly-curved capsule which has a beaked lid almost as long as the capsule itself. It is ripe in winter. When dry the leaves characteristically shrivel and curl up. It forms patches in all types of woodland, or sometimes grows as scattered plants, on loam and clay banks and by streams and rivers, but avoids highly calcareous and very acidic conditions. Very shade-tolerant, it often grows on the ground under heavy tree cover but it also inhabits woodland clearings   and other places. When fruiting it is not likely to be confused with any other species, but when barren it resembles *Mnium hornum* (p. 16) which, however, has flat, not wavy leaves. It usually grows in pure patches, but may be intermixed with the creeping stems of such species as *Eurhynchium praelongum* (p. 20).

Dicranoweissia cirrata (x 2.0) A moss forming dense, bright yellowish-green cushions and mats on tree trunks and branches in woodland and also on gate posts and thatch. It is often covered in autumn and winter with capsules. (*Photo: S.R. Edwards*)

Leucobryum glaucum (x 0.2) A moss typically forming cushions, sometimes massive, on moorland and on leaf mould on the woodland floor. Its pale, greyish-green shoots, which on drying become almost white, make it easily recognized. (*Photo: S.R. Edwards*)

Fissidens taxifolius (x 2.0)

Fissidens taxifolius is a very common moss, especially in the lowlands, and belongs to a genus that is readily recognized by its strictly two-ranked arrangement of leaves which are placed vertically on the stems and lie in one plane. The shoots thus look flattened and resemble small fern fronds. The species forms light-green to reddish-brown patches on heavy basic soil, and is common in woods where it occurs both on rides and on the ground, but also grows on banks, on roadsides, in fields and in limestone grassland. Very rarely it is found on mountain slopes but always avoids substrates that are strongly acidic. *Fissidens taxifolius* is usually less than 15 mm high and under a lens the midrib, running up the centre of each leaf and slightly out of the leaf apex, should be discernible, but microscopic examination may be necessary for definite identification. Fruit is commonly produced in winter, the red seta arising from near the base of the stem.

Dicranella heteromalla (x 3.2)

This is a very common and widespread species which resembles many *Dicranum* species in its finely pointed leaves which are curved like a sickle and point in one direction. But it is often much smaller than these, often less than 20 mm high and its leaves are finer and silkier. It forms dense bright green silky tufts or patches on base-deficient soils on banks in woodland where it may be locally dominant. It is also found on the woodland floor, occasionally on rotten logs and stumps, and on sandstone rocks and banks, on moorland and heath and in grassland, but almost always in acidic conditions. It is frequently covered with curved orange capsules which ripen in winter, each on a pale greenish-yellow seta. When old the capsules deepen in colour and becomes strongly furrowed. Its fine silky leaves and yellow setae make the plant easy to identify. *Dicranella heteromalla* is frequently associated with *Lepidozia reptans* (p. 34) and *Campylopus* species (p. 15).

Tetraphis pellucida (x 5.0) A common moss of rotting wood which at the apices of its sterile shoots produces small leafy cups containing minute gemmae, which serve to propagate the plant asexually. (*Photo: M.C.F. Proctor*)

Plagiomnium undulatum (x 1.7) This conspicuous moss with long, tongue-shaped, undulate leaves forms extensive patches on shaded soil-covered rocks. On drying the leaves become very crisped. (*Photo: M.C.F. Proctor*)

Dicranum scoparium (x 1.2)

One of our commonest mosses *Dicranum scoparium* is a very variable species, resembling in its typical form a small growth of *Dicranum majus* (p. 14) but with shorter leaves (5-10 mm long) which, though almost always turned to one side, are less regularly sickle-shaped than in *D. majus*. Some forms with straighter leaves may resemble *Campylopus flexuosus* (p. 15) in the field and these and poorly-grown colonies may need microscopic examination for definite identification.   The species forms bright yellowish-green, dense tufts 20-100 mm tall on soil, on tree trunks and branches, logs, rocks and walls in woodland, heathland, grassland and in other habitats throughout the British Isles. It is commonly barren but fruit is frequently produced in the wetter parts of the British Isles. Capsules are produced singly (see *D. majus*) in summer to winter, each borne on a reddish-yellow seta.

Dicranum majus *(x 0.9)*

This is a large handsome moss, frequently about 80 mm high but occasionally
up to 150 mm, which is hardly to be confused with any other lowland species.
It forms loose, bright yellowish-green turfs or tufts in acidic habitats, on the
ground, on logs and tree bases and on rocks in woodland, and on cliff ledges
and banks in other sheltered places. It is especially characteristic of valleys with
sessile oak woodland in the west and north but is rather uncommon in the east
and the Midlands. From *Dicranum scoparium* (p. 13) it differs in being taller
and looser in habit, with the leaves much longer (up to 15 mm long), more
sickle-shaped and more uniformly pointing in one direction. It frequently
produces capsules, ripe in late summer to autumn, and these are borne on pale
yellow setae in groups of up to five arising from a single female inflorescence;
in all other related species the fruit is produced singly.

Campylopus flexuosus (x 2.1)

Though not restricted to woodland this widely distributed moss is frequently
found in woods where it forms tufts or small patches, most commonly on peaty
woodland banks, tree bases and rotting stumps. It also flourishes in turf and on
peaty soil on rocks and wall-tops in heaths and moorland. Though its habitat is
varied it is restricted to substrates that are acidic in reaction. It is very variable,
too, in size and in colour though it infrequently exceeds 40 mm in height. It is
commonly bright mid to dark green above (often brown below, inside the tufts)
and has straight, rigid leaves that are frequently deciduous either singly or in
groups (as shown in the photograph) which serve to propagate the species
vegetatively. Fruit is occasionally produced in winter and spring and the
capsules are borne on wavy setae.

15

Mnium hornum (x 2.0)

This common and often abundant moss, is often the dominant species on ground and banks in woodlands where it forms dense, robust tufts. It also grows on stumps and at the base of trees, sometimes on rotting wood and occasionally amongst rocks and in rock crevices. But it probably always grows in acidic conditions. The young growth in spring is pale green but with age the shoots become dark green. The erect stems, matted together below, not very branched and up to 50 mm high, bear crowded leaves up to 4 mm long at the apex and shorter, less crowded leaves lower down. The leaves, which become twisted but not crisped when dry, bear strong teeth on their margins. The two sexes are borne on different plants and the terminal rosettes, which bear the male organs, and the conspicuous cylindrical drooping capsules, which are produced in spring on the female plants, may be commonly found. Confusion may arise between this species and *Atrichum undulatum* (p. 8) when the plants are barren.

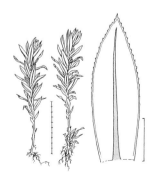

Thuidium tamariscinum (x 1.8)

Though possibly initially confused with other species, this handsome moss, one of the first noted by the beginner, is very distinctive when its main characters are learned. These are the robust habit, the broad, regularly branched (2- or 3-pinnate), flattened shoots, and bright yellowish-green colour. It is a common species throughout the British Isles forming wefts on shaded ground, more rarely on tree trunks, rotting logs and boulders, in woodland on heavy clay soils, occasionally amongst grass in the open. It is more frequent on acidic soils than on alkaline ones where it is often replaced by other *Thuidium* species. The shoots can reach to 200 mm long but are normally about 100 mm, and the often thrice-pinnate branching of the frond-like shoots often gives them a congested appearance. Fruit is rarely produced. This species may be confused with *Eurhynchium praelongum* (p. 20) but that has weaker shoots of a deeper green colour and is less elaborately branched.

Isothecium myosuroides *(x 0.9)*

This is a common, slender to medium-sized moss which has a system of primary stems that creep along the substrate and which give rise to secondary erect stems that branch irregularly and are about 10 to 20 mm high. These numerous upright shoots are finely pointed, rather congested, often slightly curved and frequently point in the same direction and these characters combine to give the plant a distinctive, rather untidy, appearance. Under a lens the leaves will be seen to be narrow and drawn out into fine points. It forms loose, pale yellowish to mid-green mats in acidic places, on tree trunks and branches, and on stumps and boulders in shaded habitats. It is a characteristic species of sessile oak-woods in western Britain where it is sometimes extensive and locally dominant. The capsules, which are slightly curved and borne on reddish setae, are not uncommon. It may be confused with *Hypnum mammillatum* (p. 27) but that species has strongly curved leaves.

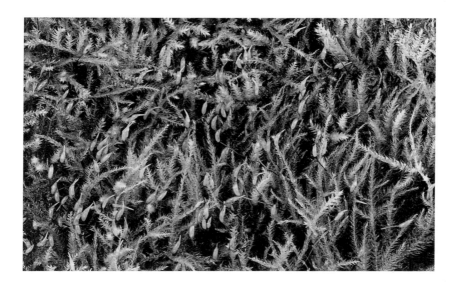

Brachythecium rutabulum (x 1.2)

With practice this moss may be recognized without much difficulty though its characters are not easily defined and it may resemble other species. It is irregularly branched and its broadly ovate, glossy leaves of a bright green or yellowish colour, which spread out widely in both wet and dry conditions, give it a characteristic appearance. It is a quite robust species, almost ubiquitous in the lowlands and abundant in many places, forming sometimes extensive patches or occasionally growing as scattered stems, especially on the ground, on tree bases, stumps and decaying branches, and on stones and rocks in woodland. It is especially fond of willow and elder. Other habitats include sheltered brickwork and stone walls, ditch sides and hedgebanks, and lawns and fields. It is common in marshes, heathlands, moorland and amongst sea-cliff vegetation. *Brachythecium rutabulum* is frequently found barren but commonly produces capsules which ripen in winter and which are borne on setae up to 30 mm tall and which under a lens will be seen to be rough.

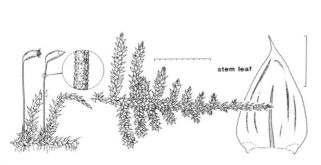

stem leaf

Eurhynchium praelongum (x 1.6)

A widespread species, *Eurhynchium praelongum* is one of commonest mosses in the British Isles. Its flattened, slender shoots are up to 100 mm long and have a regularly pinnate branching pattern, which gives them the appearance of fine fern fronds, making the species generally easy to recognize. Another characteristic feature is the dimorphic nature of shoot and leaf: the main stems are comparatively thick and have broad, widely triangular leaves, while the branches are finer with slender, narrower leaves. It forms light to dull green wefts on fertile soil, stones, stumps and logs, rarely on living wood, in woodland, hedgebanks, stream sides and in grassy places. It is very tolerant of shade and may be the only species present on deeply-shaded earth banks. Fruit is uncommon but is sometimes produced in winter in humid habitats. In its pinnate branching the species resembles *Thuidium tamariscinum* (p. 17) but the colour of *E. praelongum* is a deeper green, the shoots are more slender and the branching pattern simpler.

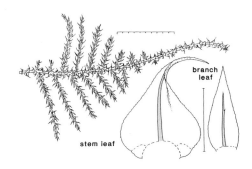

branch
leaf

stem leaf

Eurhynchium striatum (x 1.4)

Medium-sized to relatively robust this moss is found throughout the British Isles where, however, it is more common in the south and west. It forms dark green, coarse, rather glossy masses composed of freely-branched stems that give the plant a bushy appearance. The rigid leaves, which are widely triangular to heart-shaped, are seen under a lens to be strongly ridged longitudinally, especially when the leaves are dry, and to have strongly toothed margins. The slightly curved chestnut-brown capsules are not rare and each is borne on a stout seta up to about 35 mm long. In woods it is often the dominant moss on the ground but is also occasionally found on woodland rocks and in hedgerows. More rarely it grows in limestone grassland, on grassy sea-cliffs and elsewhere but prefers substrates that are at least moderately rich in nutrients. It is rarer on the more acidic soils. It sometimes resembles *Brachythecium rutabulum* (p. 19) but may be distinguished by the leaves which are of a different colour and shape and which have strong, regular striations.

Eurhynchium swartzii (x 1.7)

A rather common moss of lowland districts, especially in the southern half of Britain, *Eurhynchium swartzii* is found in similar situations to *E. praelongum* (p. 20), a species with which it sometimes grows. It forms lax yellowish-green to green patches or grows as straggling shoots and is a rather untidy species, with branching less regularly pinnate and the branches much coarser than in *E. praelongum.* Also, *E. swartzii* is more glossy when dry and prefers more open situations. Both stem and branch leaves are widely ovate, though the branch leaves are smaller, and they are spreading, in both wet and dry conditions and tend to be flattened out all in one plane. The fruit, which matures in winter, is rare. This species grows on soil and stones in woodland, occasionally on rocks and walls and on damp soil in fields, by streams, and on banks and shaded roadsides. It can be rather troublesome to identify in the field before experience is gained, and the use of a microscope may be required for definite identification.

Isopterygium elegans (x 1.2)

Confined to acidic habitats this medium-sized moss forms silky pale-green mats
with shoots that are up to about 15 mm long and grow close to the substrate
with the branches all pointing in one direction. The leaves are flattened in one
plane and often point downwards when moist; those at the tips of the branches
are often the palest and are then distinct from the lower, darker, leaves, and
give the colony a characteristic appearance. *Isopterygium elegans* frequently
produces bunches of thread-like shoots from within the leaves. These shoots
(not shown in the photograph), bear minute leaves, serve to propagate the
species vegetatively and are often so abundantly produced that they give the
mat a fluffy appearance. The plant may cover a wide area on the ground, tree
trunks and banks in woodland, and on peat and rock ledges. It prefers shaded
conditions and is often associated with *Dicranella heteromalla* (p. 11), and with
Diplophyllum albicans (p. 37) and other liverworts.

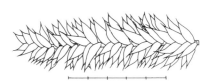

Plagiothecium undulatum (x 1.7)

One of the easiest mosses to recognize owing to its greenish-white shoots that
are more or less flattened in one plane and lie close to the substrate, this robust
species forms large, soft spreading masses on the ground and rocks in
woodland (especially of sessile oak), on shaded banks (often amongst grass), in
wet moorland and bog, and on mountain ledges. It is commonest in the west
and north of Britain and always grows in acidic habitats. The stems are sparsely
branched, up to 120 mm long, and bear crowded and overlapping leaves that
are rather large, up to about 3 mm long, and strongly undulate in both wet and
dry conditions - one of its most distinctive features. It is almost always
identifiable by eye alone and unlikely to be confused with any other species. It
often fruits luxuriantly in summer, producing long, curved capsules borne on
reddish setae up to 50 mm long. It is often associated with *Rhytidiadelphus loreus*
(p. 33) and *Dicranum majus* (p. 14).

Pseudoscleropodium purum *(x 1.5)*

Pseudoscleropodium purum, one of the most abundant mosses, is also one of the most easily recognized, with its tumid, pale bright green to yellowish, pinnately branched stems with blunt tips. It forms lax patches, often amongst grass, on banks or in short turf in a variety of habitats but is often abundant in woodland rides or in open places in woods and heathland. It will not tolerate deep shade but seems indifferent to soil, being found equally commonly on acid soil in woodland and in grassy places on chalky soil. The stems reach up to 150 mm long but are frequently less, and are prostrate to slightly ascending. The concave leaves are quite large, about 2 mm long, are broadly ovate and under a lens will be seen to have a broadly rounded tip with a short protruding point. Fruit is very rarely produced. Confusion with *Pleurozium schreberi* (p. 26), with which it is occasionally associated, is possible, but that species has a red stem and usually pointed branches. *Pseudoscleropodium purum* often also grows in association with *Dicranum scoparium* (p. 13) on heathland.

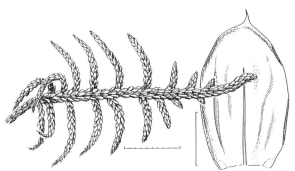

***Pleurozium schreberi* (x 1.2)**

This regularly pinnate moss may be readily known by its bright red stems which can be easily seen through the leaves. It is a common and often locally dominant species in suitable habitats in which it forms coarse, glossy, pale green to yellowish wefts. It is a species of acidic places and may be used as an indicator of acidic conditions. One of the commonest species of bryophytes in heathland habitats it also grows in moorland and on banks in woodland and is often associated with grasses and with ericaceous plants. The shoots are medium-sized, up to 120 mm long though often much smaller, and are usually upright. It may be confused with *Pseudoscleropodium purum* which, however, is a softer, more prostrate plant and has greenish stems. *Pleurozium schreberi* often grows with *Hypnum jutlandicum* (p. 27) in heathy places and with *Rhytidiadelphus loreus* (p. 33) in highland forest.

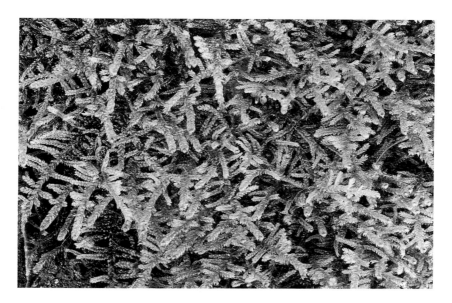

Hypnum jutlandicum (x 1.5)

Hypnum jutlandicum is a medium-sized moss which forms lax, pale green mats composed of regularly pinnately branched shoots that are flattened in one plane. When dry the plants take on a pale silvery-green appearance. As in *Hypnum mammillatum* (p. 28) the leaves are concave and curved and overlap one another, turning regularly downwards on the stems. This gives the shoots a characteristic appearance and produces the typically hooked tips of the stems and branches. It differs from *H. mammillatum*, however, in its colour and habitat. *Hypnum jutlandicum* is a widespread species, commonest in the west and south, in grassland, on heaths and moorlands often in montane habitats, and on litter, more rarely on tree bases and rocks in woodland. It always grows in acidic conditions, and is often associated with ericaceous plants.

Hypnum mammillatum (x 1.2)

This generally distributed moss is apparently most common in the west and south, forming yellowish-green to green mats on trees, logs, rocks and walls in shaded places. There are two forms. The first is very slender and has many long vertical, thread-like branches which lie parallel to each other and close to the substrate. The second is medium-sized and spreading with irregularly pinnately branched stems which lie prostrate or slightly erect. They both have curved, sharply pointed leaves which turn downwards and when in fruit the short conical lid to the capsule is characteristic. Unfortunately the fruit, though commonly produced in winter on the spreading form, is rare on the slender form and barren colonies can be named with certainty only under the microscope. The photograph shows the slender form. *Hypnum jutlandicum* (p. 27), which may resemble the spreading form of *H. mammillatum*, differs in being much paler and more regularly pinnately branched and also in its habitat.

Hookeria lucens *(x 3.3)* A moss of shaded and sheltered places with strongly flattened shoots and large, broadly rounded, translucent leaves. The cells of the leaf are very large and can be seen without a lens. (*Photo: S.R. Edwards*)

Cirriphyllum piliferum *(x 1.5)* A species of woodland clearings this moss has each leaf abruptly narrowed at the apex to form a prominent hair. The hairs project from the shoot apices in a characteristic way. (*Photo: M.C.F. Proctor*)

Rhytidiadelphus squarrosus (x 1.0)

The very distinctive way in which the apex of each leaf bends outwards to make a right-angle with the leaf base gives the apex of the shoot a characteristic star-like appearance from above, and makes this plant unlikely to be confused with any other woodland species. It is a widely distributed and abundant moss forming wide, often extensive, green to yellowish-green patches, or growing as single stems, in moist grassy places such as turf and grassy banks in open woodland, on roadside and in heaths. It is often common in lawns, mown turf, and in heavily grazed pastures, and tolerates a wide range of soils from acidic to alkaline. The plants are robust, with slender shoots up to 150 mm long and are normally ascending; the stems (which are red beneath the leaves) are irregularly branched. Capsules are very rare. Poorly-grown *R. loreus* (p. 33) may resemble this species but its leaves are curved and not bent back across the middle, and its shoot apex never appears star-like.

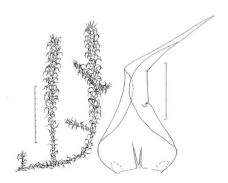

Pellia epiphylla (x 2.0)

Pellia epiphylla is a thallose liverwort which is abundant in all except calcareous places (where it is replaced by another species of *Pellia*, *P. endiviifolia*). Relatively robust it has a branched thallus a few centimetres long and up to 10 mm wide with a slightly notched apex, and which is dark green in its older parts and paler green when young. It sometimes forms extensive sheets on moist acidic soil and rock outcrops, on shaded stream banks in woodland, often on wet, sticky clay, and also on moist peaty ground in mountainous districts. The female organs are produced on the upper side of the thallus near its apex where they are protected by a flap-like structure (see the photograph). The male organs are in cavities just behind the female (they are not present in the photograph). Glossy blackish spherical capsules borne on fragile transparent setae up to 50 mm high are common in spring.

Calypogeia muelleriana (x 2.2)

This common liverwort forms flat, small to extensive, brownish-green mats, and is often mixed with other species. Its unbranched stems are about 20 mm long and on each the leaves, which have rounded apices, are crowded in two lateral rows and overlap in such a way that the apical margin of one leaf lies over the basal margin of the leaf above it (this is known as an incubous leaf arrangement). On the underside of the shoots, which are closely appressed to the substrate, there is a row of underleaves, visible with a lens when the shoot is carefully removed from the substrate. The species grows on acidic soil and peat in woodland, on banks, rocks and in heathland. It is occasionally found on decaying wood and is frequent to common in the west and north. *Calypogeia fissa*, another common species, may be confused with *C. muelleriana*, but can usually be separated by having notched tips to the leaves. *C. muelleriana* is often associated with other bryophytes including *Mnium hornum* (p. 16), *Lepidozia reptans* (p. 34) and *Dicranella heteromalla* (p. 11).

Rhytidiadelphus loreus (x 3.2) A robust moss usually with pinnate branching and curved leaves which often point in the same direction. It grows on the woodland floor and is most frequent in upland woods of the west and north. (*Photo: M.C.F. Proctor*)

Rhytidiadelphus triquetrus (x 3.0) A large, often luxuriant, moss with large, pale yellowish green, widely spreading leaves, frequent on calcareous clay banks. Its stout, rigid stems and the close branching pattern give the plant a bushy appearance. (*Photo: S.R. Edwards*)

Lepidozia reptans (x 4.4)

A lens is often required to make out this pale yellow-green liverwort which, though it may form wide and dense mats, is very small. When magnified its fine pinnately branched shoots up to 30 mm long are seen to have minute clasping, hand-shaped leaves, each with three or four lobes like stubby fingers pointing downwards and forwards towards the stem apex. It is strictly calcifuge and one of the most widespread and frequent liverworts in acidic conditions, especially in the west and north, growing as patches or scattered amongst other bryophytes on soil, peat, rotten wood, moist banks and bases of trees in woods, moorland and heaths. In spring and summer it may produce perianths and fruit but these are rather rare.   It is not likely to be confused with any other common species, especially when the structure of its leafy shoots have been seen under a lens. It often grows with *Dicranella heteromalla* (p. 11) and *Calypogeia* species (p. 32) on acid banks.

34

Lophocolea cuspidata (x 1.9)

This liverwort is pale whitish- or yellowish-green, especially when drying, and translucent. Its much-branched shoots are up to 30 mm long, but usually less, and have two lateral rows of leaves obliquely set on the stem with each leaf 2-pronged at its apex. On the underside of the stem is a row of smaller, deeply notched underleaves. A widespread species it grows in rather compact low mats on decorticated logs, stumps, exposed roots and bases of trees, and on shaded rocks in woodland, also in hedgerows and quarries and on moorland. Perianths are freely produced and capsules are common, ripening in spring and early summer. The perianth is 3-angled and its mouth has many irregular long teeth. *Lophocolea cuspidata* may be confused with *L. heterophylla*, which grows in similar places, but that species has perianths fringed with short teeth at the mouth and usually some of its leaves at the apex of the stem are without lobes, whereas those of *L. cuspidata* are all 2-lobed.

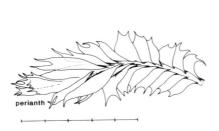

perianth

Metzgeria furcata (x 3.4) This yellowish-green thallose liverwort with its narrow, evenly forked, strap-shaped stems, is common on tree trunks, less frequent on rocks, on which it forms patches closely appressed to the substrate. (*Photo: S.R. Edwards*)

Frullania dilatata (x 3.7) A conspicuous leafy liverwort with stems usually closely appressed to tree bark. It is often of a dull green to reddish brown colour and resembles a diminutive *Calypogeia* species. (*Photo: S.R. Edwards*)

Diplophyllum albicans (x 3.0)

Perhaps the commonest British liverwort of non-calcareous places this species occurs in a wide range of habitats. Its shoots are whitish- to yellowish-green to dark green or slightly brownish, to 50 mm long (though usually much shorter) and are usually upright in humid situations but may be prostrate in drier places. Individual shoots may be slightly branched and each shoot is flattened and has two very regularly arranged lateral rows of leaves. However, there may at first sight appear to be four rows of leaves. This is because each lateral leaf is divided deeply into two lobes, the upper of which lies upon the lower. It frequently produces perianths which are furrowed at the apex, the capsules ripening in late spring. *Diplophyllum albicans* grows in dense turfs or patches in woodland on moist rocky banks and rock faces, boulders and soil, very rarely on stumps and logs. Elsewhere it may be found in bogs, on heaths and in the mountains. It often grows intermixed with other bryophytes and bears a superficial resemblance to the moss genus *Fissidens* (p. 10).

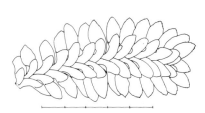

Plagiochila porelloides (x 2.0)

Common in the west and north this widespread liverwort has somewhat
ascending, occasionally branched, stems up to about 50 mm long with two
lateral rows of spreading leaves. Each leaf is rounded in outline, without lobes,
and its margin is usually slightly toothed (use lens!). Perianths and capsules are
rarely produced but perianths are present in the photograph (please refer to
the drawing for their position on the stems). The plant forms swollen, dense
mats on alkaline to slightly acidic rock outcrops in woodland, amongst rocks in
moorland, in stream gullies and on walls and boulders in shaded places,
especially in woodland. It is abundant in limestone districts and is generally
one of the most common leafy liverworts with undivided leaves. This species
and *P. asplenioides* (p. 39) are sometimes extremely similar in appearance but
the latter is much larger.

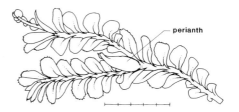

perianth

Plagiochila asplenioides   (x 1.6)

This handsome liverwort probably attains the largest size of all British species of leafy liverworts and from its size alone is hardly to be confused with any other. It is similar to the closely related *P. porelloides* (p. 38), but is larger, with shoots up to 120 mm long and nearly 10 mm wide. The unlobed leaves, which are in two rows on the stem, are arranged in each row like the tiles on a roof with the basal margin of one leaf lying over the apical margin of the leaf below it (this is known as a succubous leaf arrangement). Most leafy liverworts in the British Isles possess this type of leaf arrangement which is clearly shown in the photograph. It is much less widespread and abundant in the north than *P. porelloides* though it is frequent in the west and south where it grows in acidic to basic conditions on soil and rocks in sheltered, humid places in woods, on banks, in ravines and in turf. Perianths and capsules are very rare.

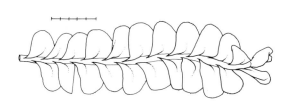

Index